CALVIN AND HOBBES SUNDAY PAGES 1985-1995

CALVIN AND HOBBES SUNDAY PAGES 1985-1995

An Exhibition Catalogue by

BILL WATTERSON

SCHOLASTIC INC.
New York Toronto London Auckland Sydney
Mexico City New Delhi Hong Kong Buenos Aires

ISBN 0-439-38111-8

12 11 10 9 8   5 6 7/0

Printed in the U.S.A.   08

First Scholastic printing, January 2002

Design: Frank Pauer

This catalogue accompanies the exhibition *Calvin and Hobbes: Sunday Pages 1985-1995* at The Ohio State University Cartoon Research Library from September 10, 2001, to January 15, 2002.

The exhibition was mounted with the support of The Ohio State University Libraries. All works in the exhibition are from the personal collection of the cartoonist, and we are grateful to him for lending them for this purpose. We also appreciate the contributions of Frank Pauer, Marilyn Scott, Erin Shipley, Dennis Toth, Rick VanBrimmer, and Richard Samuel West to the exhibit and this publication. Special thanks to Andrews McMeel Publishing for producing and distributing this book.

Cover: [unpublished watercolor of Calvin and Hobbes] Private collection. Watercolor on paper. 12 x 12.4 cm.

PREFACE

Everyone misses *Calvin and Hobbes*.

It reinvented the newspaper comic strip at a time when many had all but buried the funnies as a vehicle for fresh, creative work. Then Bill Watterson came along and reminded a new generation of what older readers and comic strip afficionados knew: A well-written and beautifully drawn strip is an intricate, powerful form of communication. And with *Calvin and Hobbes*, we had fun—just like readers of *Krazy Kat* and *Pogo* did. Opening the newspaper each day was an adventure. The heights of Watterson's creative imagination took us places we had never been. We miss that.

This book is published in conjunction with the first exhibition of original *Calvin and Hobbes* Sunday pages at The Ohio State University Cartoon Research Library. Although the work was created for reproduction, not for gallery display, it is a pleasure to see the cartoonist's carefully placed lines and exquisite brush strokes. In an attempt to share this experience with those who are unable to visit the exhibition, all of the original Sunday pages displayed are reproduced in color in this book so that every detail, such as sketch lines, corrections, and registration marks, are visible. On the opposite page the same comic strip is printed in full color. Because Watterson was unusually intentional and creative in his use of color, this juxtaposition provides *Calvin and Hobbes* readers the opportunity to consider the impact of color on its narrative and content.

When I first contacted Bill Watterson about the possibility of exhibiting his original work, I used the term "retrospective." He replied that we might be able to do an exhibit, but that calling it a retrospective made him uncomfortable since it has been only a few years since he stopped drawing the comic strip. He felt that a longer time was needed to put *Calvin and Hobbes* in the historical perspective implied by that term. Nonetheless, this show is a "look back" at the comic strip as we revisit favorites that we remember. *Calvin and Hobbes: Sunday Pages 1985-1995* is particularly interesting because each work that is included was selected by Bill Watterson. His comments about the thirty-six Sunday pages he chose are part of this volume. In addition, he reflects on *Calvin and Hobbes* from the perspective of six years, and his essay provides insights into his life as a syndicated cartoonist.

Reprint books of *Calvin and Hobbes* are nice to have, but the opportunity to see the original work and read Bill Watterson's thoughts about it is a privilege. He generously shared not only the art, but also his time and his thoughts. When I first reviewed the works included in the exhibit, I knew that everyone who visited it would begin with laughter and end with tears.

On behalf of all who enjoyed *Calvin and Hobbes*, thank you, Bill Watterson.

Lucy Shelton Caswell
Professor and Curator
The Ohio State University Cartoon Research Library
June 2001

CALVIN AND HOBBES SUNDAY PAGES 1985-1995

It's been five years since the end of *Calvin and Hobbes*, the longest time I can remember in which I haven't drawn cartoons. *Calvin and Hobbes* was a wonderful experience, but it was an all-consuming career. When I quit the strip, I put my cartoons in boxes, and jumped into other interests. I haven't really considered the strip since, so at the invitation to do this show, I thought it might be time to look back at some of my work.

My first reaction in going through my old cartoons was some amazement at the size and weight of the pile. For most successful comic strips, ten years is just a drop in the bucket, but even that amount of time yields a huge amount of material. It's no wonder that decade seems like a blur.

Going through my old strips is sort of like looking at old photographs of myself: they're personal and familiar, yet somewhat bizarre at the same time. There are cartoons I've drawn that are the equivalent of pictures of my younger self wearing yellow pants: I know I'm responsible for that, but what on earth was I thinking? As my tastes have changed, and as I've learned more, I imagine that I would do many strips quite differently today. Not better necessarily, but certainly differently. I was twenty-eight when *Calvin and Hobbes* was first published, and, of course, I would make other choices now at age forty-three.

It's also sort of strange to see a record of my own learning curve. Pick up a given strip, and I see how I struggled with various writing and drawing problems, or how I finally surmounted one. I remember sometimes feeling that the strip was better written than I could actually write, and better drawn than I could actually draw. I learned a great deal over the years by trying to push the strip beyond my own abilities, and I'm very proud that *Calvin and Hobbes* explored and developed all the way to the end. By the final years, I see naturalness or a sense of inevitability to the drawing and writing that is very satisfying. I'm more appreciative of this kind of grace since returning to the awkward stages of new learning curves.

Of course, I'd also say the times have caught up with some of my strips. It's frankly a little discouraging to see how ordinary some of them look now. When *Calvin and Hobbes* first appeared, it was somewhat surprising to treat reality as subjective, and to draw a strip with multiple viewpoints, juxtaposing Calvin's vision with what others saw. I did this simply as a way to put the reader in Calvin's head and to reveal his imaginative personality. Now these juxtapositions are a visual game for many comic strips, and after all these years, I suspect readers know where this sort of joke is headed as soon as they see it. The novelty cannot be recaptured.

Novelty, however, is probably overrated anyway. The *Calvin and Hobbes* strips that hold up best, to my eye anyway, are the ones where the characters seem big, vivid, and full of life, and where the strip's world seems genuine and inviting. Punchlines come and go, but something in the friendship between Calvin and Hobbes seems to hold a small piece of truth. Expressing something real and honest is, for me, the joy and the importance of cartooning.

The Sunday strips were usually the cartoons I had the most fun with, and for this show I've chosen a few Sunday strips from each year that I think show off the strip's strengths.

I have fond memories of reading the Sunday comics when I was a kid. As far as I was concerned, the Sunday comics were the whole reason for newspapers to exist. On weekdays, I read only the strips I liked; but on Sundays, I read them all, and often several times. The Sunday comics were always the most fun to look at, so when I finally got the chance to draw my own comic strip, I knew I wanted to make the Sunday *Calvin and Hobbes* something special.

It took me a little while to learn to use the larger Sunday space effectively. It requires a somewhat different pace for the humor, and, of course, a big color panel is no place to find out that you don't know how to draw the back of your character's head. The Sunday strip shows off both strengths and weaknesses.

Occasionally I would see that an idea I'd written for a Sunday strip was not as substantial as I'd hoped it would be, and I'd realize that some of the panels and dialogue weren't adding anything significant to the story. If that were the case, I'd remove everything extraneous and use the trimmed idea for a daily strip instead. I held the Sundays to a different standard: any idea for the Sunday strip had to need the extra space. I felt a Sunday strip should do something that was impossible the rest of the week.

Over the years, I learned that daily strips are better suited for certain kinds of ideas, while Sunday strips are better for others. The daily strip is quick and to the point, perfect for a simple observation, or a short exchange between characters. Daily strips are also better for long stories, where a certain suspense can be fostered by continuing the story day after day, and the reader can remember what happened previously.

Extended conversations with real back and forth dialogue, however, don't work very well in four tiny panels—the dialogue balloons crowd out the drawings and the strip loses its grace. In a Sunday strip, you can spread out, and let the characters yap a bit. This is often funny in itself, and it's a wonderful way to let the characters' personalities emerge. It also lets you explore a topic a bit more fully.

You can talk about things without reducing them to one-liners right away.

And, of course, in today's minuscule comics, if an idea requires any real drawing, the Sunday strip is the only possible place for it. Likewise, any complex storytelling problem—a strip illustrating a long expanse of time, for example, or an event depicted in a succession of very tiny moments—is futile in the daily format. Calvin's fantasies generally migrated to the Sunday page for this reason.

In short, the Sunday page offered unique opportunities, and I deliberately tried to come up with ideas that could take advantage of them.

I usually wrote the Sunday strips separately from the dailies. For the daily strips, I tried to write an entire month's worth of ideas before inking any of them. This allowed a long period for editing and rewriting. I was less able to do this for the Sunday strips because the Sundays need to be drawn weeks further in advance and because the strips took so much longer to draw. If at all possible, however, I would try to keep two or three Sunday ideas ahead of the deadlines. I always wanted to reserve the option of abandoning an idea that didn't stand up to a few weeks of scrutiny.

For those who are interested in technical matters, the early strips were drawn on any cheap pad of Bristol board the local art supply store happened to stock. The paper was usually rather thin and sometimes the sheet wouldn't accept the ink consistently (bad sizing or something), which would make drawing aggravating and time consuming. Eventually I switched to heavier Strathmore Bristol board, which was much nicer. I used a 2H pencil to rough in the drawing, and then inked with a small sable brush and India ink. I did as little pencil work as possible in order to keep the inking more spontaneous, although the more elaborate panels required more preliminary drawing. For lettering, I used a Rapidograph cartridge pen. I drew the dialogue balloons and a few odds and ends with a crow quill pen. To cover up unwanted marks, I used various brands of Wite-Out, and in the early days, typewriter correction fluid. (Remember typewriters?) No doubt this stuff will eat through the paper or turn green in a few years, but as the original cartoons were intended for reproduction, not picture frames and gallery walls, I did not overly concern myself with archival issues or, for that matter, neatness. At some point along the way, however, I did ask the syndicate to send the printers a quality reproduction of the Sunday cartoon, rather than the original drawing, in order to reduce the amount of tape, registration marks, and general crunchings and manglings to which the drawings had previously been subjected.

Coloring the strips was a slow and tedious process. My syndicate gave me a printed sheet showing

numbered squares of color, each a mixture of various percentages of red, yellow, and blue. Using this sheet as a guide, I taped some tracing paper over the finished cartoon, and painted watercolor approximations of the available colors in the areas I wanted. This would give me a very rough idea of what the newspaper version might look like. Then I numbered each little spot of color. As the Sunday strips became more visually complex, and as I started to use color more deliberately for effects, this process became a real chore. These days, I believe much of it can be done with a few clicks of a mouse.

Colors take on different characteristics when placed next to other colors (a neutral-seeming gray might look greenish and dark next to one color, but brownish and pale in relation to another). Because of this, I came up with one little trick for coloring the strip. I cut out each of the color squares provided by the printer, so I had a stack of colors (like paint chips), rather than a sheet. By laying out the cut squares and physically placing one color next to the others I expected to use, I could see exactly how each color behaved in that particular context. As I got better at this, I was able to choose appropriate "palettes" for each strip, and create moods with color. One strip might call for contrasting, bright colors; another strip might be done with a limited group of soft, warm colors; another idea might call for a close range of grays and darks, and so on. If I made Calvin's skin a dull pink-gray to suggest dim lighting at night, I would have to find a dull yellow-gray that would suggest his hair in the same light. These challenges took an inordinate amount of time for work on deadline, but I was often quite proud of the results. A comic strip should always be fun to look at, and good use of color can contribute to that appeal. More than that, color creates its own emotional impact, which can make the drawing more expressive.

The half-page Sunday format required certain guaranteed panel divisions. The strip had to be drawn in three rows of equal height, and there was one unmovable panel division within each row. This allowed editors to reduce and reconfigure the strip to suit their particular space needs. The same strip could run in several shapes by restacking the panels.

Editors commonly removed the entire top row altogether, so in essence, a third of the strip had to be wasted on "throwaway panels" that many readers would never see. The fixed panel divisions were also annoying because they limited my ability to compose the strip to best suit the idea. For example, they often forced a small panel where I needed more space for words.

Of course, a big part of cartooning is learning to work effectively within tight space constraints. Much of cartooning's power comes from its ability to do more with less: when the drawings and ideas are

distilled to their essences, the result can be more beautiful and powerful for having eliminated the clutter. That said, there is a point at which simplification thwarts good storytelling. You can't condense *Moby Dick* into a paragraph and get the same effect. Over the years, my frustration increased and I became convinced that I could draw a better comic strip than the current newspaper format was permitting. Looking at examples of comics from the 1930s, when a Sunday strip could fill an entire page, I was amazed by the long-forgotten possibilities out there.

I took a sabbatical after resolving a long and emotionally draining fight to prevent *Calvin and Hobbes* from being merchandised. Looking for a way to rekindle my enthusiasm for the duration of a new contract term, I proposed a redesigned Sunday format that would permit more panel flexibility. To my surprise and delight, Universal responded with an offer to market the strip as an unbreakable half page (more space than I'd dared to ask for), despite the expected resistance of editors.

To this day, my syndicate assures me that some editors liked the new format, appreciated the difference, and were happy to run the larger strip, but I think it's fair to say that this was not the most common reaction. The syndicate had warned me to prepare for numerous cancellations of the Sunday feature, but after a few weeks of dealing with howling, purple-faced editors, the syndicate suggested that papers could reduce the strip to the size tabloid newspapers used for their smaller sheets of paper. Another strip could then run vertically down the side. Consequently, while some papers, primarily in larger markets, ran the strip as a half page, other papers reduced it. In some of the latter papers (including the one I read at the time), I actually lost ground: the new Sunday strip was printed even smaller than before. I was in no mood to take on new fights, so I focused on the bright side: I had complete freedom of design and there were virtually no cancellations.

For all the yelling and screaming by outraged editors, I remain convinced that the larger Sunday strip gave newspapers a better product and made the comics section more fun for readers. Comics are a visual medium. A strip with a lot of drawing can be exciting and add some variety. Proud as I am that I was able to draw a larger strip, I don't expect to see it happen again any time soon. In the newspaper business, space is money, and I suspect most editors would still say that the difference is not worth the cost. Sadly, the situation is a vicious circle: because there's no room for better artwork, the comics are simply drawn; because they're simply drawn, why should they have more room?

Business controversies aside, the new format opened up new ways to tell stories, and I drew different

kinds of strips as a result. I could write and draw the strip exactly as I imagined it, so it truly challenged my abilities. Whereas Sunday strips had previously taken me a full day to draw and color, a complex strip would now take me well into a second day to finish. Deadlines discourage this kind of indulgence, and I had to steal that extra time from what would have been some semblance of an ordinary life, but I was thrilled to expand the strip's world.

Laying out the panels became a job in itself, now that I was no longer confined to horizontal rows. I could place boxes anywhere and any size, but the reader's eye needs to flow naturally to the proper panels without confusion, and big panels need to be designed in such a way that they don't divert attention and spoil surprises. The graphic needs of each panel must be accommodated and the panels themselves should form a pleasing arrangement so the entire page is attractive, balanced, and unified as well. Here again I looked for guidance in the gorgeous Sunday pages of George Herriman's *Krazy Kat*.

The new Sunday format necessitated a change in the format of my book collections as well. Having won a bigger strip in newspapers, I wanted the book reproductions to reflect the strip's new impact as much as possible by printing the Sunday strips large. This resulted in the rather awkward horizontal format of my later books. They stick out of bookshelves, but the strips look nice. From this point on, the Sunday strips were reproduced in color with each collection, not just in the "treasury" collections, as before. (Here's a piece of trivia: because of the timing of the book format change, the cartoons from the *Snow Goons* collection were never put in a treasury book, so those Sunday strips have been reprinted only in black-and-white.)

Ten years after starting *Calvin and Hobbes*, I ended the strip. As much as I knew I'd miss the characters, the decision was long anticipated on my part. Professionally, I had accomplished far more than I'd ever set out to do and there were no more mountains I wanted to climb. Creatively, my interests were shifting away from cartooning toward painting, where I could develop my drawing skills further. And personally, I wanted to restore some balance to my life. I had given the strip all my time and energy for a decade (and was happy to do so), but now I was that much older and I wanted to work at a more thoughtful pace, out of the limelight, and without the pressures and restrictions of newspapers.

The final *Calvin and Hobbes* strip was a Sunday strip. The deadline for Sunday strips being early, I drew it well before writing the daily strips that would eventually precede it in the newspaper. I very much wanted to hit the right note for this final strip. I think it worked, but it was a bittersweet strip to draw.

Since *Calvin and Hobbes*, I've been teaching myself how to paint, and trying to learn something about music. I have no background in either subject, and there are certainly days when I wonder what made me trade proficiency and understanding in one field for clumsiness and ignorance in these others. On better days, I enjoy having so many new challenges and surprises. Even so, these new endeavors have only deepened my appreciation for comics. I no longer take quite so much for granted the versatility of comics and their ability to depict complex ideas in a beautiful, accessible, and entertaining form. For all their seeming simplicity, the expressive possibilities of comics rival those of any other art form. Five years after *Calvin and Hobbes*, I love the comics as much as ever.

Bill Watterson
Summer 2001

CALVIN AND HOBBES
SUNDAY PAGES 1985-1995

DECEMBER 29, 1985

I drew this about a month into the strip, when *Calvin and Hobbes* appeared in a few dozen newspapers. My own newspaper didn't carry the strip, which made my job feel very abstract.

The first two panels, composing the entire top row, are the "throwaway" panels that many newspapers would eliminate to make the strip smaller. Knowing that few readers would see it, I often wasted most of the space up there, but here I've drawn a nice little series of Calvin carrying on. The lower panels are all the same size. This was not an aesthetic decision; I really didn't know what else to do. Fortunately, lack of drawing ability is rarely a liability in cartooning, and this arrangement, while unimaginative, is nevertheless effective in its simplicity and clarity. Also notice that, in a single strip, we learn something about the personality of all three characters. From the beginning, *Calvin and Hobbes* was more about characters than jokes, and I think this was an important reason the strip was able to attract an audience and survive the tough first years.

This was drawn when President Reagan was staring down the Soviet Union with an arms buildup. It all seems very long ago now … thank heavens.

On the original drawing, you can see that the word "okay" has been whited out and changed to "OK," making the little bulge at the end of the balloon unnecessary. The syndicate apparently felt that OK was more correct than okay. Eventually I learned to write it that way myself and save the syndicate some trouble.

April 13, 1986

Note the pads on Hobbes's hands. I liked those as reminders that his hands were really paws, but I soon decided that the black circles were visually disruptive, and prevented the hands from being read and understood instantly. The pads stayed on Hobbes's feet, but hands are too expressive to clutter up.

May 18, 1986

This was the introduction of Calvin's babysitter, Roz. She doesn't even have a name here, as I never expected to use her again. Her ferocious personality surprised me though, so she came back several times.

At that point, I used her for longer stories, continuing across daily strips, where the conflicts could play out on a larger scale.

Notice the rotary telephone and the television with UHF and VHF channel knobs. These were outdated even in 1986, but I think they're funnier looking, and have more personality, than the new ones. I think my parents were the last people in America to watch a black-and-white TV, so old appliances fit the strip that way, too.

FEBRUARY 1, 1987

Calvin and Hobbes doesn't seem that long ago, but here we are with an LP in the first panel. The drawings from this strip were often ripped off for illegal T-shirts and the like.

I wanted a page of drawings that flowed into each other, but you can see the gaps (in the middle of the second row and at left in the third row) where panel divisions were mandated. By this time, the characters were becoming more physically three-dimensional in my mind, and I had fun animating them.

February 15, 1987

This is one of the rare Sunday strips where the pictures don't do much of the work. A purely verbal strip is tolerable once in a while for variety, but boy, the writing had better be working hard.

July 5, 1987

The Spaceman Spiff episodes were always fun to draw. I never really took the stories anywhere, but I loved drawing the landscapes, monsters, and spaceships. The landscape here is invented and rather generic, but in later strips, southern Utah became a great inspiration. The long throwaway panel at the top shows the type of scale and atmosphere one can evoke with a bit more room. Remove it, as many papers did, and the strip looks much more static and restrained.

September 27, 1987

This strip was part of a story that was continuing across the daily strips. The daily strips were sold separately from the Sunday strips, and newspapers did not always buy both. Consequently, readers might be seeing the whole story, all of the story except this strip, or this strip and none of the story. Thus, the challenge for me was to make this strip integral to the plot, yet entirely self-sufficient, yet utterly expendable. I believe I succeeded, although I'm hard-pressed to say why I bothered.

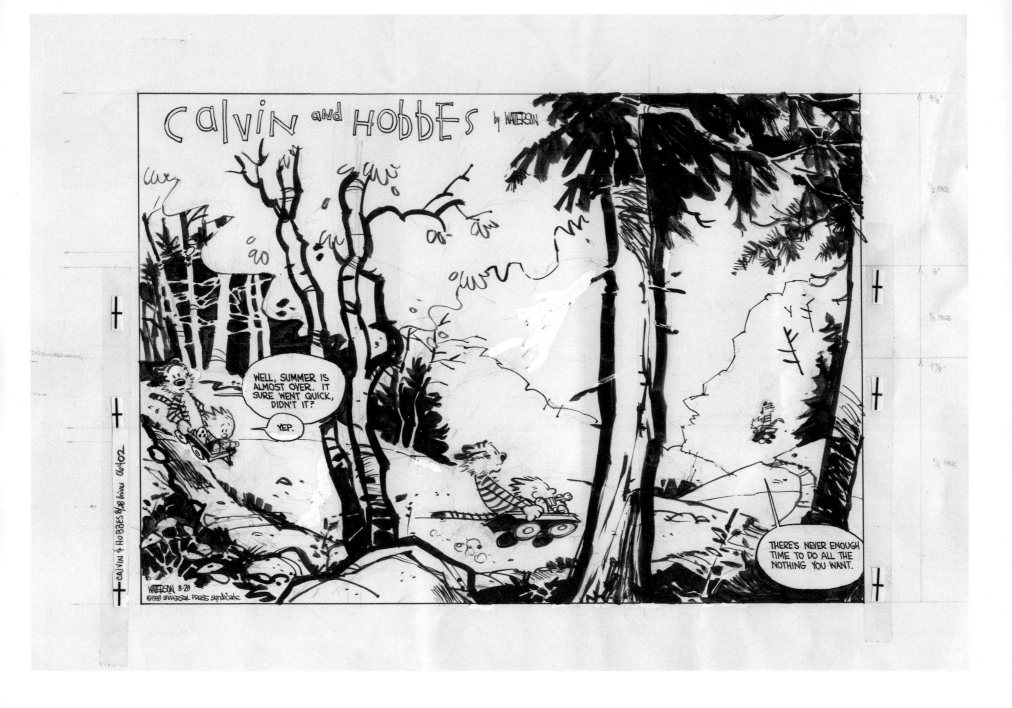

AUGUST 28, 1988

I liked the idea in this strip enough to put it in a Sunday strip, but it's very simple and I didn't want to pad it with the number of panels the usual format required. To draw the strip as one large panel, I had to condense all the words and action at the very bottom, so editors could hack away at the rest of the drawing if they wanted to print a smaller strip. On the edge of the original, you can see where I've marked the various page divisions. As is, the strip would run as a half page of the newspaper. Take off the top (the "throwaway panels") and the strip would run as a third of a page. Lop off another inch and a half, and the bottom part can be printed as a quarter page. The trick was to compose the drawing so that it would look intentional no matter how it was cropped.

This strip presented a further problem when it came time to be reprinted in a book collection. The strip, no matter how it's cropped, is horizontal, but the books had either a square or vertical format. The only solution was to redraw the whole thing in a vertical format for the books.

MARCH 26, 1989

40

Several of my favorite Sunday strips depict an entire day. It's a slightly different way of telling the story, as there is no real plot. Instead, numerous isolated moments are illustrated, and the connection between them is largely made in hindsight. The Sunday strip offers enormous flexibility in storytelling, and this gradually attracted more and more of my interest.

June 4, 1989

calvin and Hobbes

by WATTERSON

AHHHH...

UH-OH. SOMETHING IS SERIOUSLY WRONG HERE.

THE LAWS OF PERSPECTIVE HAVE BEEN REPEALED!

OBJECTS NO LONGER DIMINISH IN SIZE WITH DISTANCE!

LINES DO NOT CONVERGE TOWARD ANY POINT ON THE HORIZON!

ALL SPATIAL RELATIONSHIPS ARE LOST! IT'S IMPOSSIBLE TO JUDGE WHERE ANYTHING IS! OH NO!

CALVIN, QUIT RUNNING AROUND AND CRASHING INTO THINGS, OR I'LL SELL YOU TO THE MONKEY HOUSE!

...AND NOW *SHE'S* LOST PERSPECTIVE.

It's surprisingly tricky to draw things exactly wrong, because you have to know the rules pretty well to break every single one. The strip was fun to draw.

With every strip, my goal is to surprise myself. If I'm not surprised, the reader surely won't be either. The surprises are usually fairly small, so it's a real delight when an idea pops in from Pluto. The soap opera drawing style, the ludicrous dialogue, the bizarre storyline—every part of this strip confounded expectations. I hoped the reader would wonder for a second if *Calvin and Hobbes* had been replaced by another strip.

I wish I'd drawn this with a bit more flair in the line work. Some of the old continuity strips were very stylishly drawn and I'd like to have captured that. What I didn't know at that time was that many of those cartoonists drew very large. Doubling or tripling the size of my original would have helped.

September 10, 1989

Here I was beginning to get a little more adventurous with panel layout, although I was still constrained by the mandated space divisions. The open spaces and different box shapes give the strip a looser feel. When the strip was restacked in some papers and in the book collections, the visual rhythm could go out of whack. Open panels might be next to each other, and boxed panels might all line up on the left side, and so on. The flexibility of the format always had a price.

May 13, 1990

As I went along, I started eliminating dialogue from Sunday strips. Words are essential for certain kinds of ideas, but it is good to remember that cartoons are a visual medium, and pictures can do a great job of telling a story all by themselves.

June 17, 1990

Drawing this strip required a trip to the library to see some examples of cubist art, as I'd once again written material over my own head. The idea for this strip came from my tendency to examine issues until I'm incapacitated by the persuasiveness of all sides.

September 16, 1990

December 30, 1990

Calvin and Hobbes
by WATTERSON

I ASKED DAD IF HE WANTED TO SEE SOME NEW YEAR'S RESOLUTIONS I WROTE. HE SAID HE'D BE GLAD TO, AND HE WAS PLEASED TO SEE I WAS TAKING AN INTEREST IN SELF-IMPROVEMENT. I TOLD HIM THE RESOLUTIONS WEREN'T FOR *ME*, THEY WERE FOR *HIM*.

THAT'S WHY WE'RE OUTSIDE NOW.

I *WONDERED* WHAT THE RUSH WAS.

I'M GETTING DISILLUSIONED WITH THESE NEW YEARS.

THEY DON'T SEEM VERY NEW AT ALL! EACH **NEW** YEAR IS JUST LIKE THE **OLD** YEAR!

HERE ANOTHER YEAR HAS GONE BY AND EVERYTHING'S STILL THE SAME! THERE'S STILL POLLUTION AND WAR AND STUPIDITY AND GREED! THINGS HAVEN'T CHANGED!

I SAY WHAT KIND OF FUTURE *IS* THIS?! I THOUGHT THINGS WERE SUPPOSED TO IMPROVE! I THOUGHT THE FUTURE WAS SUPPOSED TO BE BETTER!

©1990 UNIVERSAL PRESS SYNDICATE

WATTERSON 12-30

THE PROBLEM WITH THE FUTURE IS THAT IT KEEPS TURNING INTO THE PRESENT.

FEBRUARY 3, 1991   Unlike most art, comics often lose something in the original. In newspapers the last panel was in color.

CALVIN AND HOBBES

by WATTERSON

CALVIN SUDDENLY REALIZES THE WORLD HAS NO HUE, VALUE, OR CHROMA!

HAVE THE PHOTORECEPTORS IN CALVIN'S EYES STOPPED WORKING PROPERLY, OR HAS THE FUNDAMENTAL NATURE OF LIGHT CHANGED ??

PERHAPS SOME STRANGE NUCLEAR OR CHEMICAL REACTION ON THE SUN HAS CAUSED ELECTROMAGNETIC RADIATION TO DEFY SEPARATION INTO A SPECTRUM!

MAYBE OBJECTS NO LONGER REFLECT CERTAIN WAVELENGTHS! WHATEVER THE CAUSE, IT'S CLEAR TO CALVIN THAT THERE'S NO POINT IN DISCUSSING THINGS WITH HIS DAD!

THE PROBLEM IS, YOU SEE EVERYTHING IN TERMS OF BLACK AND WHITE.

SOMETIMES THAT'S THE WAY THINGS ARE !!

To draw this strip, I not only avoided color and halftones, I avoided outlines. As the top "throwaway" panels illustrate, the placement of black is crucial to making the pictures comprehensible.

During my fight to prevent *Calvin and Hobbes* from being turned into licensed merchandise, I was accused of having a black-and-white view of the issue. The arguing dragged on for years and was very frustrating and unpleasant, so it was a bit of a release to get an interesting strip idea out of the conflict.

April 19, 1992

This strip was done in the new half–page format. It has only six panels, but I think the space is used attractively.

To an editor, space may be money, but to a cartoonist, space is time. Space provides the tempo and rhythm of the strip. Used well, it directs the eye to speed up or linger. The long drawing of Hobbes walking away is a sort of visual brake. It's empty, so the eye rests there and the panel creates a pause.

May 24, 1992

Although conservative in panel layout, I could now use the entire space without threat of having panels removed or rearranged for different newspaper formats. Readers would finally see everything I drew, exactly the way I drew it.

There are lots of words in this strip. That's always somewhat visually oppressive, but the dialogue has some spirit and I think there's enough going on to reward the reader's patience. The color helped enliven the drawings too. I'd have used more black if this were intended to remain uncolored.

I usually saved the G.R.O.S.S. strips for longer stories in the dailies, but the new space in the Sundays was an irresistible opportunity to let the characters bounce off each other for a while.

December 6, 1992

I think much of the fun in this strip comes from the details in the drawing. The visual richness encourages you to look at the strip for a moment even after you get the joke. This pleasure is largely lost now that newspapers print the comics so small.

December 13, 1992

With the large Sundays, I felt that *Calvin and Hobbes* kicked into high gear. The large format not only encouraged new ways of presenting ideas, it forced me to push the drawings, to make Calvin's world as bold and energetic as I could. I felt the strip finally looked the way it did in my head.

March 21, 1993

I can't read this strip without thinking of the cat who inspired much of Hobbes's personality. Sprite was an exuberant gray tabby we had. Enlarge her to tiger size, and this is what things would be like. The last panel drawing looks just like her.

This strip gave me my favorite book title.

April 11, 1993

AT 35,000 FEET, THE ENGINES OF FLIGHT 430 EXPLODE FOR NO REASON!

WITH PLUMES OF DENSE SMOKE TRAILING FROM THE WINGS, THE GIANT AIRCRAFT PLUMMETS OUT OF CONTROL!

MEANWHILE, A 50-CAR FREIGHT TRAIN HITS A PENNY ON THE RAIL AT 80 MILES AN HOUR AND JUMPS THE TRACKS, DRAGGING HALF A MILLION TONS OF METAL INTO THE AIR BEHIND IT!

calviN and HObbEs

by WATTERSON © 1993   4·11
distributed by universal press syndicate

IN A FREAK COINCIDENCE, BOTH THE JET AND THE TRAIN ARE CONVERGING ON *ONE SPOT*,...WHERE TECTONIC PLATES IN THE EARTH'S CRUST HAVE JUST BEGUN TO SHIFT!

THAT SPOT IS THE HOUSE OF FARMER BROWN, WHO, AT THIS MOMENT, IS UNAWARE OF A GAS LEAK AS HE ATTEMPTS TO LIGHT HIS STOVE!

AS HE STRIKES THE MATCH, HE CASUALLY GLANCES OUT THE KITCHEN WINDOW.

HIS EYE TWITCHES INVOLUNTARILY.

CAN'T WE PLAY SOMETHING ELSE?

calvin and hobbes by WATTERSON ©1993
dist. by universal PRESS Syndicate 7·4

July 4, 1993

I like the little touches in these drawings—the octopus legs trailing out of the fridge, the use of a plumber's helper as a cooking utensil, the notion that shrunken heads might be sold in jars, etc. As you might guess, I was an unappreciative little kid once.

AUGUST 15, 1993

Count 'em: nineteen panels. You can draw a big, fat summer day in nineteen panels. This strip would have a very different feel with less space.

November 7, 1993

I sometimes tried for the spare visual effect of a Japanese print—very few things, but precisely placed. In November strips, I always tried to capture that austere, gray, brambly look that Ohio gets.

February 6, 1994

The choice between good and evil was a recurring theme in the strip, and nothing tested Calvin like a good slushball.

March 6, 1994

This is one of the weirdest strips I drew, and I'm not exactly sure I understand it myself, but it still makes me laugh, so there you are.

January 1, 1995

The dinosaur strips always took forever to draw, since I had to imagine and construct them from skeleton diagrams and other illustrations. They were a lot of fun if the deadlines weren't right on top of me. This one was a little tricky, because the T. Rex anatomy doesn't fit easily into an airplane cockpit, and it required a little fudging.

May 14, 1995

If I had any extra room to spare, I'd try to make the panel design interesting. Here the large black rectangle visually separates Calvin's school day from his time at home. The crooked panels and heavy use of black are tricks I learned from *Krazy Kat*. This sort of design can be distracting and annoying if not handled with restraint. The panels can be interesting, but they should never divert attention from the drawings.

Whenever the strip got ponderous, I put Calvin and Hobbes in their wagon and sent them over a cliff.
It had a nice way of undercutting the serious subjects, and it often doubled as a visual metaphor as well.
Plus, it's a lot more fun to draw than a series of talking heads.

September 24, 1995

This strip has a lot of back and forth conversation, and the idea was to create a sense of escalating lunacy. Once again, you can't do this sort of thing in just a few panels. Nor would this work across several daily strips—you'd lose the momentum. The large Sunday format captured the spirit of *Calvin and Hobbes* in ways that had been impossible before.

November 5, 1995

November 19, 1995

Another strip with no words at all. I kept the panel design extremely clean and simple, so nothing gets in the way of the frantic story. I'm very pleased with how each moment is distilled. A lot of experience fed into each picture by this point.

December 31, 1995

This was the final strip of *Calvin and Hobbes*. I typically colored panel borders and word balloons, but in this strip, I left everything white. Only the characters and the sled were colored, so the drawing would have a very spare and open look to mirror the ideas in the dialogue.

SELECTED BIBLIOGRAPHY

Calvin and Hobbes comic strips by Bill Watterson were collected and reprinted in the following volumes, all of which were published by Andrews McMeel Publishing:

Calvin and Hobbes. 1987.
Something Under the Bed Is Drooling. 1988.
The Essential Calvin and Hobbes. 1988.
Yukon Ho! 1989.
The Calvin and Hobbes Lazy Sunday Book. 1989.
Weirdos from Another Planet! 1990.
The Authoritative Calvin and Hobbes. 1990.
Scientific Progress Goes "Boink." 1991.
The Revenge of the Baby-Sat. 1991.
The Indispensable Calvin and Hobbes. 1992.
Attack of the Deranged Mutant Killer Monster Snow Goons. 1992.
The Days Are Just Packed. 1993.
Homicidal Psycho Jungle Cat. 1994.
The Calvin and Hobbes Tenth Anniversary Book. 1995.
There's Treasure Everywhere. 1996.
It's a Magical World. 1996.

Additional information about Bill Watterson and his work may be found in the following:

Richard Marschall. "Oh, You Kid: A Strip of Leviathan Quality, *The Comics Journal* 127 (February 1989), 72-77.
Bill Watterson. "Calvin and Hobbes," CARTOONIST PROfiles 68 (December 1985), 36-41.
———. "Some Thoughts on *Pogo* and Comic Strips Today," CARTOONIST PROfiles 80 (December 1988), 12-19.
———. "The Cheapening of the Comics," *The Comics Journal* 137 (September 1990), 93-98.
Richard Samuel West. "Interview: Bill Watterson," *The Comics Journal* 127 (February 1989), 56-71.
———. "Errors and Misconceptions," *The Comics Journal* 130 (July 1989), 52.